Behind the High Street

KENNETH HUDSON

THE BODLEY HEAD
LONDON SYDNEY
TORONTO

ACKNOWLEDGMENTS

Thanks are due to the following for supplying photographs: Trafford Park Estates Ltd, page 4 (bottom); Neil & Spencer Ltd, back cover (bottom left) and page 13 (top); G. H. Mobbs, back cover (top right); Mrs Joan Moran, page 5 and 33 (bottom); Northampton Museums and Art Gallery, pages 6 (bottom) and 11 (centre top); Central Electricity Generating Board, pages 7 (top) and 42 (top); Kodak Limited, pages 7 (bottom) and 14; J. Sainsbury Ltd, pages 8 (top) and 9 (top and bottom); Tesco Limited, page 8 (bottom); Unilever, page 8 (centre left); C & J Clark, page 11 (top and bottom right); Bollom Ltd, page 12 (top); CDS Launderettes, page 12 (bottom); Kayser Hosiery Manufacturers, page 15 (top); Courtaulds, Limited, page 15 (bottom); South Western Gas, page 18 (top); East Midlands Gas Board, page 18 (bottom); *Bath Chronicle*, page 20 (top); British Airways, page 22 (top); *The Times*, page 22 (bottom); HMV Shops Ltd, pages 3 (bottom) and 23 (bottom); EMI Limited, page 24 (top and bottom); Bath Reference Library, pages 25 and 46 (bottom); National Westminster Bank, pages 27 (bottom) and 28 (top); Trustee Savings Bank Group, page 28 (bottom); *Illustrated London News*, page 30 (bottom); J. Wolff & Son Ltd, pages 4 and 32; G. & J. Geddis, page 34; Henry Pool & Co, Savile Row, pages 35 (top) and 36 (bottom); Leeds Reference Library, page 36 (top); University of Southampton, pages 37 (bottom) and 38 (top left); The Boots Co. Ltd, pages 38 (bottom left), 39 and 40; South Eastern Electricity Board, page 41 (top right); Electricity Council, back cover (centre left) and page 41 (bottom); Pedigree Pet Foods, page 42 (bottom); Metal Box Limited, page 43 (top); The Ford Motor Company, page 45 (top left); British Leyland Motor Corporation, back cover (top left) and page 45 (top right); Henlys Ltd, page 45 (bottom), and Smith's Food Group, page 47 (bottom right). All other photographs © Ann Nicholls 1982.

British Library Cataloguing
in Publication Data
Hudson, Kenneth
Behind the High Street
1. Shopping centres – Bath (Avon) –
History
I. Title
381'09423'98   HF 5430.6. G7
ISBN 0–370–30394–6

Text © Kenneth Hudson 1982
Printed and bound in Great Britain for
The Bodley Head
9 Bow Street, London WC2E 7AL
by William Clowes (Beccles) Ltd
Set in 14 on 16 pt Ehrhardt
First published 1982

Contents

What is behind the High Street?

The High Street is the part of the town where most of the shops and activity are to be found. There may or may not be a street actually called the High Street. When people talk about 'the High Street' nowadays, all they mean is the main shops.

So this book is about the buying and selling that goes on in the centre of town. It concentrates on one particular town, Bath, because this is where I live and I know more about it than I do about other towns. During the past thirty years especially, Bath, like other towns, has changed a great deal. The shops don't have the same kinds of customers as they used to and people want to buy different things. More and more shopping is done in supermarkets and less in small specialist shops.

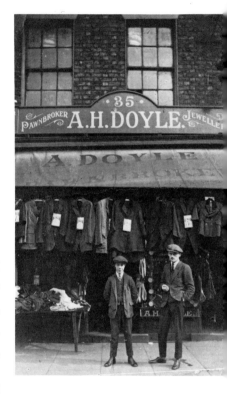

In 1945, most shops were still small shops, sometimes with just one window by the side of the entrance and sometimes with two windows, one at either side of the door. There was always an assistant to serve you; self-service shops were unknown and, largely for this reason, there was hardly any shoplifting. The proprietor or manager often lived over the shop, which is rarely the case these days.

The supermarkets and the chain stores have caused great changes in the High Street. They need an enormous amount of floor-space and they can sell many things considerably cheaper than the small shop can. So the past thirty years has seen a steady disappearance of the kind of small shops which were in competition

with the big national concerns and a great deal of rebuilding and conversion to create the sort of premises the big firms need. Some kinds of business, however, can carry on perfectly well in a small shop. Newsagents, hairdressers and antique dealers are good examples.

It's very interesting to pick out a number of today's shops, covering as wide a range as possible, and then to go to the Public Library and, with the help of local street directories, find out what was going on at each of these addresses, ten, fifty or a hundred years ago. What you discover is likely to be always pretty much the same, wherever you live, although the details are bound to vary from place to place. This book shows only some of the possibilities. When you start carrying out the same sort of detective work in your own town, you'll certainly come up with a lot of surprising information.

Any kind of shop, no matter what its size, must have things to sell. A hundred years ago many shops made at least some of their goods on the premises or in a local workshop. They were self-contained. Bootmakers made boots, bakers made bread, butchers killed and prepared their own meat, milliners and tailors made clothes. This is now rare. A shop has become the centre of a spider's web, buying its goods from all over the country, and from abroad. Shops are changing all the time, and behind them the firms and industries that supply them are also changing.

For each of the shops mentioned in this book, I have suggested some of the directions in which our explorations behind the High Street can go. A garage takes us back to the places and companies which make cars and supply petrol, an outfitter's to the factories that provide the clothes, an electricity showroom to the firms who specialize in cookers, toasters and vacuum cleaners. And, like the shops, each of these separate industries has its history, too. One of the questions we should always be asking ourselves when we are in a shop is 'Where did these things come from?' And today the answer is just as likely to be Tokyo, Milan or Taiwan, as Birmingham, Leeds or Newcastle. 'Behind the High Street' these days often means several thousand miles behind it.

(*Above*) Interior of J. Sainsbury's, Guildford, circa 1906

A supermarket

Supermarkets in Britain are hardly thirty years old. In 1950 they had just arrived from the United States, but there were not many of them and, by American standards, they were tiny. But during the Fifties the situation changed fast. Skilled counter assistants were hard to find and they had to be paid high wages. So we followed the American example. We made the customers serve themselves and everything that could be canned or packaged was. The new plastic packaging

A typical Mac Fisheries' store in the 1950s

An early Tesco's shop ▷

materials, like polythene, were coming on the market at this time and that made the development of self-service shops much easier.

And, as the supermarket came in, the little food shops moved out. Most of the food chains, like the Home and Colonial Stores, the Maypole Dairies and Liptons, that our grandparents knew so well, disappeared altogether and new names—Tesco, Safeway, Waitrose—entered the High Street. One or two of the old-established firms lasted a long time. Mac Fisheries, for instance, only went out of business in 1980, and a very few, like Sainsbury's, adapted themselves to the new pattern of shopping and prospered.

Before the Second World War, Sainsbury's shops, with their gleaming tiles and wide space between the counters were the most up-to-date in the business. Now there are only two of them left from this period, and their days are numbered. Sainsbury's stores, like those of their competitors, get bigger and bigger, and where there is no room for expansion and rebuilding, the old shops are sold off and the company starts again on a bigger site. The branch of Sainsbury's in Bath, for example, is a modern building, because converting old premises doesn't work for this kind of shop, where there has to be a lot of floor-space and no dividing walls.

The old Sainsbury's shop in Drury Lane, London, which was demolished in the 1970s

◁ Present-day Sainsbury's in Bath

A shoe shop

This particular shoe shop has changed with the times. The present firm was established here in the 1920s. In the Twenties and Thirties, well-to-do people had their boots and shoes made specially for them, and Barratts was very much that kind of business. Now, however, it does what every other shoe shop does—buys its stock from the factory.

In the mid-Fifties there were about a thousand firms in Britain making footwear. There are about seven hundred today, and the number is going down each year, mainly because we import so many shoes from abroad. The selling of shoes, however, is in the hands of far fewer firms, and, whatever the name over the shoe shop may be, the likelihood is that it belongs to one or other of the big groups, like Freeman, Hardy & Willis, Dolcis or Clarks. More and more shoes each year are sold by supermarkets and department stores, not by shoe shops.

These days every man, woman and child in Britain buys on the average of four pairs of footwear a year. This includes everything from bedroom slippers to football boots, and it adds up to a lot of pairs. But women buy more than the average and men buy less,

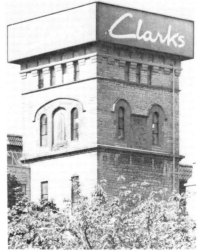

△ Shoemaker's, Northampton, 1913

(*Top*) An early Showcard for Clarks' shoes, circa 1915
(*Bottom*) Part of Clarks' present-day factory in Street

which is why there always seem to be more shops selling women's shoes.

A pair of shoes takes a much shorter time to make now than it did thirty years ago, about a tenth of the number of working hours. This is why production today is concentrated into bigger factories. They have more modern machinery and methods, and do the job quicker and more cheaply. And the lower the price, the more pairs the manufacturers hope people will buy, especially since most modern shoes can't be repaired, except in small ways, like fixing a new heel. The disappearance of the shoe-repairer, who always worked with leather, had been another important change in the High Street.

△ Bristol branch of Bollom's, 1947

Dry-cleaners

During the past fifty years, the number of laundries has steadily declined, and the number of dry-cleaning shops has equally steadily increased. The laundries have gone mainly because families have bought washing-machines, and launderettes have taken over a large slice of the business, too.

Until the Second World War, most dry-cleaning was done by laundries as a sideline, but there were two big firms who specialized in the work, Pullars of Perth and Sketchley of Hinckley, in Leicestershire. Many small shops, especially outfitter's and draper's, were agents for them. They collected clothes locally and sent them

off to Perth or Hinckley by rail, in huge baskets. It was our wonderful pre-war railway service that made dry-cleaning possible.

Since 1945, the cleaning industry has been completely reorganized. What brought about the change was a compact machine, known as the Spencer Mark One Junior, which was first available in 1949. This allowed routine cleaning to be done in the shops, instead of having to be taken to a factory. The cleaning firms then set up their own chains of shops, which could be run by two people, and only specialized work had to be sent away.

One day there will be a dry-cleaning machine which can be used in the home and which will be as safe and easy to use as the washing-machine already is. And when that happens the cleaners' shops will disappear from our High Streets just like the laundries have.

The Spencer Mark One Junior, which revolutionized the dry-cleaning industry.

A photographic shop

This early eighteenth century building was originally a house and then spent nearly a hundred years as a butcher's, with the shop below and living accommodation overhead. The butchery business lasted until the early Fifties, when the premises were taken over by a photographic dealer.

Making and selling photographic equipment has been one of the world's biggest growth industries during the past thirty years. If you look in your local photographic shop, the chances are that you'll find that a high proportion of the cameras sold there are Japanese, but this is a new development. Before the Fifties, most of the equipment and film used in Britain was British, American or German, and a great deal of it still is.

For half a century Kodak was the great name. Kodak film and cameras were being made in Britain by 1903. The company's main British factory operating today was established at Wealdstone, near Harrow, in Middlesex in 1905. When Kodak first went to Wealdstone the factory looked out over farms. There was a clean, dust-free atmosphere, good railway connections with London, and the fifty-five acre site seemed adequate to meet all future requirements. But with the enormous growth of the photographic industry it was soon too small and the Company now employs thousands of people on three other locations.

Kodak factory at Wealdstone

A clothes shop

Fifty years ago, shops selling women's clothing were concerned almost entirely with natural materials — cotton, wool, silk and linen. The steady switch to synthetic fibres has been a feature of the post-war period, and nowadays it's almost as difficult to imagine a world without nylon and Terylene as one without detergents.

Rayon was first available commercially in 1905, although until 1924 it was always called 'artificial silk'. Nylon dates from 1937 and Terylene from 1940, although both materials were reserved entirely for military use in Britain during the war years. As a result, nylon stockings were not easily available here until ten years after women in America had been wearing them.

During the past fifty years the small dress shop has been under intense competition from the chain stores. Marks and Spencer began selling women's clothing in 1939 and during the Thirties British Home Stores and Littlewoods were also selling the cheaper lines of dresses, blouses and shirts. Except in the North, the big department stores went mainly for a middle–class market.

(*Above*) Early 1960s advertisement for nylons
(*Below*) Courtaulds' main factory at Coventry, 1908

But the small, specialist dress shop somehow managed to survive, usually because it has been willing to take risks with colours, fabrics and designs which would be too dangerous for the big stores, which deal in very large quantities, where too-frequent mistakes and too much daring would lead to bankruptcy.

This particular shop has changed tenants and uses many times since the building was put up in the 1820s. In the 1880s, for example, it was a women's hairdresser's, in the 1930s an optician's, and in the Seventies a boutique. It now belongs to Laura Ashley, which concentrates on traditional fabrics, especially cottons.

Bath's new gas showrooms

The old and new gas showroom

This is one of those unusual cases when the new premises are smaller than the old. There's a good reason for this. Gas is a prosperous, modern industry in Britain nowadays, but the range of domestic gas appliances isn't very wide. Most of them are concerned with cooking and heating and, once installed, they usually last a long time. People don't buy new gas equipment very often, so although the Gas Boards need to employ a large staff dealing with installation, maintenance and accounts, they have fewer people working on the sales side.

The old gas showrooms in Bath, given up in the mid-Seventies, were previously two separate shops, and

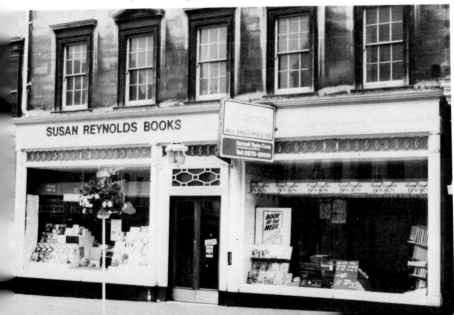

Former premises of the gas showrooms in Bath

Ideal kitchen as planned for the Home Service Exhibition at Burnley, 1936

from time to time there was another business upstairs. Today they have become a shop selling cut-price books, known as remainders. These are copies of slow-selling titles that publishers have sold off to the bookseller at vastly reduced prices.

The new, smaller showroom is in a recently built shopping precinct. A gentlemen's hatter's occupied the site for many years and then, in the 1920s, the shop became a branch of the David Greig grocery chain.

Until long after the 1939-45 war, gas had a rather old-fashioned, dirty image. Electricity was the clean, modern fuel and gas a second-best. The coming of North Sea gas in the Sixties and Seventies and the steady rise in electricity prices changed the situation. The old method of making gas from coal disappeared, the local gasworks were closed down and gas suddenly moved into the modern world.

Doncaster gas works, early 1960s

Two Post Offices

Most towns have an interesting Post Office history and the details of it usually aren't too difficult to find and piece together.

Bath's present Head Post Office was built in the 1930s. The previous main Post Office, now known as The Old Post Office, came into existence in the 1860s when two fine Georgian houses were knocked into one to accommodate it. As Bath grew and Post Office business expanded, the old building was found to be too small and inconvenient. So it was sold off and used, first, by an estate agency, then by a firm of surveyors and valuers, and after that it was taken over by the Midland Bank. But the Post Office clock is still there, giving a clue to the previous occupiers of the building.

Arrival of the London-Bristol mail van at Bath, circa 1922

When The Old Post Office was in use, there weren't any post vans. All the mail came and went by train, and the postman rode bicycles, pushed handcarts, or walked. There were no parking problems and not a great deal of mail, so it could all be sorted out on the premises without too much difficulty. But eventually, in the 1880s, a new Sorting Office had to be built near the railway station. That was given up in the Twenties and now a bookbinder and bookseller has his business there, with the new Sorting Office nearby.

The photograph below shows a small sub Post Office, which opened in the early 1920s. Before that the premises were simply a house. The GR pillar-box outside is a useful clue to roughly when the changeover happened. Nowadays this, like most sub Post Offices, sells a variety of other goods: stationery, cigarettes and sweets.

1930s postman

A travel agent

The premises of Cook's present office in Bath has been connected with travel for well over a century. Previously, the building was used first as the Great Western Railway's Receiving Office, the place in the centre of town to hand in parcels and baggage for the railway to carry, and then as the Great Western and LMS Railway's Ticket Issuing and Enquiry Office. This, of course, all changed in 1948 when our railways were nationalized.

Originally Thomas Cook were concerned with arranging people's journeys by train and boat, but these days most of their business involves air travel.

Before the Second World War, nearly all their customers travelled individually; nowadays ninety per cent of their work is concerned with package tours. In other travel agencies, the proportion is even higher.

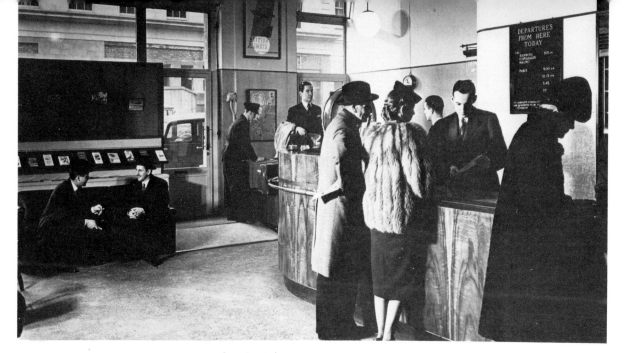

A contrast in styles: air travel then and now. (*Above*) British Airways Terminal, London, 1930s and (*Below*) present-day holiday-makers queuing at Gatwick.

And, since more than three-quarters of the people who go on package tours travel by aeroplane, airlines and airports are right in the centre of the travel agent's world.

The other big change that has affected travel agents is that all kinds and classes of people use them today, whereas before 1939 not more than five per cent of the British population at most ever went abroad at all. Thomas Cook, like other firms arranging holiday travel, have been an important part of the social revolution of our time.

A record shop

Bath has comparatively few record shops, and this is one of them. For most of last century, the building belonged to one of two local newspapers, *The Bath Herald*. Sixty years ago, the present owners bought it to accommodate their piano business and in due course records were added to pianos and sheet music. For the past twenty years, records have been the main part of the business, although in recent years tapes have become almost as popular.

(*Above and below*) EMI recording studio, City Road, circa 1904

Until the early 1950s, very few records were sold each year, compared with the huge numbers that appear now. So the shops that stocked records had to have other lines as well, in order to make a living, and the places that sold records nearly always offered gramophones as well.

Until the post-war record boom started, the industry in Britain was mostly in the hands of two companies, His Master's Voice and Columbia, which eventually merged to form EMI – Electrical and Musical Industries.

HMV was established as far back as 1898. Its early headquarters and recording studios were in London, at 31 Maiden Lane and 21 City Road. These buildings are still there, and you can see from their size what a tiny affair the record business was in those days before the First World War, when a gramophone was a great luxury. Columbia first set up in business at 102–8 Clerkenwell Road, London, in 1911. The recordings were made in a studio on the fifth floor. It had to be given up in the late Twenties, when electrical recording arrived, because of interference from the trams in the street below.

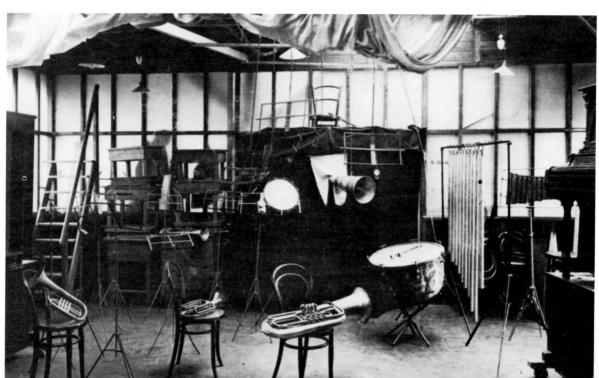

THE EMPIRE HOTEL, BATH,

IS the largest and has undoubtedly the best position of any Hotel in Bath. It adjoins the Orange Grove and looks over the Gardens, which are accessible to visitors to the Hotel. There are lovely views from almost every room of the Hotel, of the Avon, the Abbey, and the surrounding country. The Abbey, Roman Baths and Antiquities, the Corporation Hot Mineral Baths and Pump Room (the most complete in Europe), the Royal Institution Library and Museum, are close to the Hotel, while the views obtained of Prior Park, Bathwick, Widcombe, Hampton and Combe Downs, and the North Parade (where some of the scenes in "The Rivals" take place) are unsurpassed.

The Empire Hotel can accommodate over 200, and is most beautifully appointed in every respect. There is a splendid inner and outer Lounge carefully protected from draughts, and overlooking the river Avon and the Abbey. In addition there are numerous public rooms containing

EVERY COMFORT OF MODERN LIFE.

There is a Passenger Lift to all floors, constructed so that invalids may be carried into same in their chairs and taken right into the Baths. Electric Light in every room. The Diet prescribed for Invalids has been specially studied. The Hotel is heated and ventilated on modern scientific principles. Sanitation the most perfect and modern. Visitors' Servants have a special Dining Room and Reading Room. Hotel Omnibus meets all trains. Service of Trains is excellent, Bath being first stop from Paddington by quick expresses.

An hotel

An advertisement for the Empire Hotel, Bath

Many public libraries have good collections of material about local hotels and restaurants, some of it going back a hundred years or more. You can find publicity brochures, menus, prices and advertisements, which allow you to see how conditions and customers have changed over the years.

The Empire Hotel, for example, was opened in 1901. It cost £40,000 to build and it was managed by a London firm of caterers, Spiers and Pond. About two hundred people could be accommodated here in great comfort. At the time it was built it was the only hotel in Bath to have electric lifts, which were still considered to be a great luxury in 1900, and very American.

When it first opened the advertisements for the Empire Hotel made it clear that the hotel was catering for well-to-do customers, especially elderly people and invalids. The lounges were 'carefully protected from draughts' and there were special invalid diets. 'The Hotel is heated and ventilated on modern scientific principles. Sanitation the most perfect and modern. Visitors' Servants have a special Dining Room and Reading Room. Hotel Omnibus meets all trains. Service of Trains is excellent, Bath being first stop from Paddington by quick express.'

Those days have long gone. Immediately the War broke out in 1939, the guests at the Empire were given forty-eight hours to pack up and leave. The Admiralty then took over the building and have been there ever since.

In fact, it would be difficult and expensive to convert the building into a modern hotel. The rooms are too big, the ceilings too high, there are very few bathrooms and practically no parking space. You will probably be able to find similar examples in your own town of former hotels that have been converted to other uses.

The Empire Hotel as it is today

A bank

This is on a corner site in one of Bath's most fashionable streets. In the 1880s it was a millinery shop, but soon afterwards it became the Capital and Counties Bank. The first and second floors were left almost as they were, but the ground floor, where the banking goes on, was converted both inside and out, so now the building is Victorian on the street level and Georgian above that. In the Twenties the Capital and Counties Bank was taken over by Lloyds.

If you look at any of the bigger branches of banks you will find that they are mostly very grand inside, especially those which have been there for fifty years or

Surbiton, circa 1920

(*Above*) Interior of a Victorian bank

more. The high and elaborate ceilings and fine woodwork are there to impress the customers and make them feel their money is safe. If you look carefully at all the banks in your own town—most of them are likely to be in or around the High Street area—you'll see how well maintained the buildings are. A decrepit-looking bank, with stonework crumbling and the paint peeling, wouldn't be at all good for business.

It's worth noticing, too, how the newer banks, like the Trustee Savings Bank, go for a brighter, lighter, less daunting style of premises than the older banks. They're trying to impress in a different way, by telling the public how modern they are.

Two radio and television shops

One of these shops is concerned with renting television sets, so it doesn't need to have a big window display. Its workshops at the back take up more room than the shop itself. The second shop has decided not to put all its eggs in one basket. It sells other electrical appliances as well as televisions, radios and videos, in the hope that if one side of the business isn't going too well, the other will be.

Broadcasting in Britain started in 1921 and for some

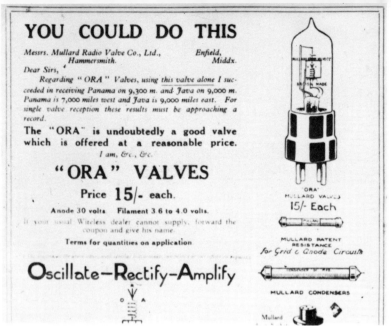

An advertisement for radio valves, 1922

time most listeners made their own sets. The early wireless shops sold parts, not complete sets. You bought a circuit diagram, which gave details of all the components you needed and how to assemble them and wire them up, and then you spent happy hours following the instructions building the set. Sometimes it didn't work straight away, and then you had to spend less happy hours finding out what was wrong. But by about 1930, when broadcasting was expanding very fast – the BBC built Broadcasting House and its first high-powered transmitters then – the amateur, do-it-yourself days had gone and you could buy a set cheaper than you could make one. The radio shops started to look more like they do today and famous manu-facturers' names were appearing in the shop windows and in advertisements, names like Ekco, Cossor, and Murphy, which have all gone now. Look through pre-war newspaper files in the library and you'll find them.

Early BBC recording studio at Savoy Hill

Three antique shops

Like all other towns and cities, Bath has a lot of problem-shops, places which are difficult to sell or find tenants for. Quite a number of these become antique shops, which sometimes prosper and sometimes close down after quite a short time.

These three are typical. Two of them, as the picture shows, are side by side. The one with the white-painted front was a bootmaker's in the 1880s, a cake shop in the 1930s and a hairdresser's in the 1970s. The dark-coloured shop was once a greengrocer's, then a hairdresser's, and then a general store. The other shop, the 'antique market', sold books and sheet music for thirty years and then, at the end of last century, became

part of a large drapery business which, in its turn, closed down in the mid-Seventies.

'Antiques' is a word which has widened its meaning in recent years. Until the 1950s it meant collectors' pieces, good quality furniture, silver, porcelain and other household objects, usually made before the reign of Queen Victoria. This is what it still means in the higher grade or, as some people would say, the *real* antique shops. In recent years, however, many so-called antique shops have been stocking what used to be called junk—very ordinary second-hand furniture and bits and pieces made at any time during the past hundred years.

At least half the 'antique' businesses, probably more, that one sees today are of the second type and these are the ones that are moving into the shops that used to be occupied by butchers and bakers and grocers. Look around your High Street and see if you can distinguish one kind of antique shop from the other.

An example of a higher grade antique shop

A building society

These particular premises haven't been occupied by a building society for very long. Before that, going backwards in time, they accommodated a trunk manufacturer, a woodworking machinist, a carpenter, and a bootmaker. But, as the photograph shows, the building is called Lombard House, and this is a clue to a very different kind of business that was once carried on here, a pawnbroker's. In the Middle Ages, many of Europe's pawnbrokers, bankers, jewellers and goldsmiths, came from the part of Italy known as Lombardy. They were the Lombards, and one of the great banking streets in the City of London is still

A pawnbroker's in Windsor Street, Liverpool, circa 1930

called after them. And a search through Bath's directories reveals that there was indeed a pawnbroker carrying on business here during the first part of the present century.

Compare the number of pawnbrokers shown in your local street directory in, say, 1900 with those in 1940 and today. Bath had six in 1900, one in 1940 and there are none at all today, which shows how much better off people are now than they used to be.

But as the number of pawnbrokers has gone down, the number of estate agents and building societies has gone up everywhere. With fewer and fewer houses available to rent, families have been compelled to buy somewhere to live and to borrow the money with which to do it. The local directory can help you here, too. Compare the number of estate agents and building societies in your town today with the number thirty or fifty years ago. The results may surprise you.

Belfast pawnbroker's, circa 1919

A men's outfitter

Burton have had a shop in Bath since the early 1930s, when they converted two small shops into one. Both the old businesses belonged to tradesmen of a type that has vanished by the hundred during the past fifty years—a family grocer and a bootmaker.

Until the 1860s, men's clothes were made either at home or in small, private workshops. The changeover to large-scale production came soon after the sewing-machine was introduced into England from America, and between then and 1914 new machines for cutting cloth several layers at a time, for high speed stitching, button-holing and sewing on buttons transformed the tailoring industry.

The centre of the new clothing factories was Leeds. Burton's factory, built in the Twenties, was the largest

△ Behind the scenes in the workshop at Henry Pool & Co, Savile Row, London, early 1940s

in the world. It covered a hundred acres and employed eight thousand people. But Burton had other factories, too. The famous Burton shops, selling what was produced by the factories, were all built to a characteristic and rather palatial design. Many of them had billiard rooms on the upper floors, to provide young men in the town with a pleasant club atmosphere in the evenings.

The billiard clubs were closed down in the early Sixties, and in recent years Burton have changed a great deal. The clothes they now sell are bought from many different manufacturers, some in Britain, some overseas. The traditional made-to-measure system is no longer the main part of the business. And the shop fronts are completely different now, compared to how they were twenty years ago.

(*Above*) Burton's factory in Leeds, 1939
(*Below*) Showroom of a Savile Row tailor in the 1950s

A computer centre

Like many of the buildings in Bath that are now shops, this one was originally a house. It dates from the 1780s and the upper part of it is badly in need of restoration. The handsome shop-front was put in when it was converted into a chemist's shop in the 1870s. It remained a chemist's, a family business, with only three owners, until 1979. By then the small chemists were being squeezed out of the market by the bigger companies like Boots, but there was a growing demand for computers and computer services, and this new business could have a prosperous future ahead of it.

Computers have now become such a part of our everyday lives that it is easy to forget that the first

A first generation computer, circa 1958

△ Cumbersome early storage tapes

electronic computer in the world was built only thirty-seven years ago. The early computers were huge, because they were valve-driven. As soon as transistors arrived in the mid-Sixties, however, computers became a fraction of their previous size. Before that, they couldn't have been sold from premises as small as the Bath Computer Centre. The equipment would have taken up far too much room and, even if you had been able to squeeze it in, the valves would have produced so much heat that the people working there would have suffocated. Shops like this selling computers and computer equipment are therefore a comparatively new feature of our High Streets.

▽ Boots' original shop in Nottingham

A chemist

This is one independent chemist who has managed to survive, probably because the site is in a very busy part of town. For the past hundred years, this particular shop has never been anything else but a chemist's. Four different firms have been there during this time.

A great change has taken place in chemists' shops during the past fifty years or so. Before that time, a chemist could make a satisfactory living by making up doctors' prescriptions and selling patent medicines, with one or two fairly profitable sidelines, like cosmetics, soap and toothpaste. This is no longer the case, and the average chemist's shop sells a vast range of goods.

This is particularly the case with the biggest company in this field, Boots. A modern Boots store is a kind of supermarket, selling everything from dog leads to cameras, with the pharmaceutical side of the business tucked away in one corner. It is very difficult for an independent chemist to compete with Boots, particularly since this giant concern manufactures such a large proportion of its pharmaceutical products itself and is therefore able to make a much bigger profit out of them.

Tablet-making factory, Nottingham, circa 1920

An old-style chemist shop

So each year more and more of the pharmaceutical business passes into the hands of Boots, and more and more private chemists close their businesses down. When you look at a shop like Stephen Kennedy's in your town, you should ask yourself two questions: 'How has it managed to survive?' and 'How much longer is it likely to be there?'

An electricity showroom

All the regional Electricity Boards have showrooms where they display and sell electrical equipment. In the 1880s the present South-Western Electricity Board Showroom in Bath was two shops, a draper's and a grocer's. Later, in the Twenties, another draper had both shops for a while, and when he gave up

Woolworths took over the premises. They stayed there until the Sixties, when they moved into a brand new and much bigger store.

The big expansion in the sale of domestic electrical appliances came in the 1950s and 1960s. During this period the proportion of households with vacuum cleaners went up from forty to seventy-two per cent, washing-machines from four to fifty per cent, and refrigerators from two to thirty-three per cent. In recent years, washing-machines and freezers have shown a similar rise in sales but, with the big rise in electricity prices, the use of electricity for heating has gone down considerably. The age of cheap electricity has probably gone for ever and, as a result, the range of goods in the Electricity Showrooms has changed a great deal during the past twenty years.

The Electricity Showroom at Mansfield, 1938

George V at Barking Power Station, 1925

But the most important fact behind the showroom is the steady rise in the number of households with electricity. In 1930 there were roughly four million, in 1950 ten million and in 1970 sixteen million, which means practically every home in the country. To have electricity in the Twenties meant belonging to the privileged classes. Nowadays, the idea of living without electricity seems absurd.

A pet shop

Until the late Forties, dogs were usually fed on scraps and dog biscuits. Cats got bread and milk and, if they were lucky, occasional bits and pieces of fish. Those days are long past. Most of what dogs and cats eat now comes out of tins and, since there are now more than five million dogs and four million cats in Britain, this is big business.

About three-quarters of what our domestic pets eat

Cat food advertisement, 1952

is made by one company, which has huge factories in Melton Mowbray and Peterborough. This firm started up in a very small way in the Thirties in a tiny factory on the Slough Trading Estate, near London. The building is still there, although it's now used for quite a different purpose, and it ought, perhaps, to be preserved as a monument to the beginnings of what is now a very large industry. It shows how the British petfood industry has grown during the past thirty years.

The Melton Mowbray factory was built in the early Fifties and the one at Peterborough in 1974. They just manage to keep pace with demand by working twenty-four hours a day, seven days a week. These two factories are among the biggest customers of another important twentieth century industry, can-making. And, of course, by putting their products into cans, they can sell through ordinary shops. Most petfood nowadays is bought from supermarkets, not pet shops. The pet shops make a large part of their living these days therefore by selling all the other things that pets need, such as brushes and leads and baskets, as well, of course, as the pets themselves. This particular pet shop in Bath adds an interesting touch of colour to the High Street scene.

Can-making factory in Worcester, circa 1934

A garage that is and a garage that was

The site for John Tallis Motors was found by demolishing a pair of old houses which had quite big gardens. The new building, put up in the Sixties, has car showrooms and workshops on the ground floor and flats on the three floors above. So far, this is a building without history. It's too young to have any.

The building below, however, has a very interesting past. It dates from the early Twenties and to make room for it a timber-yard was cleared away. The garage business was established here at a time when very few people had cars. The showrooms were elegant, partly because Bath was that kind of place and partly because the kind of people who bought cars in the Twenties and

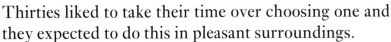

(*Top left*) Production line for Ford V8s, circa 1938
(*Top right*) Chassis-assembly shop, Cowley, 1913

Thirties liked to take their time over choosing one and they expected to do this in pleasant surroundings.

But by the Seventies the car trade had changed completely. What a garage needed then was plenty of room for workshops, parking, and petrol pumps. The scale of the business had become much bigger and a site like this one was no longer suitable. So the garage closed down and a firm selling plants and garden equipment moved in. If you look around your own town you will probably find similar examples of buildings which used to be garages and which are now used for some quite different purpose.

Another interesting change is that nowadays it's quite normal for a garage to concentrate on selling just a single make of car. Many manufacturers, indeed, insist on this. So, as the picture shows, at John Tallis Motors it's Volvo.

Two pubs

Pubs stay pubs, whatever other changes there are in the High Street and among the brewers. These two, the Saracen's Head and Ye Old Farm House, have both been here for getting on for four hundred years, but there is an important difference between them. The Saracen's Head is in its original building, but Ye Old Farm House was pulled down and rebuilt in 1892.

Originally most pubs brewed their own beer. Later it became normal for each town to have at least one brewery of its own. Then, with the expansion of the railways between 1830 and 1860, it became possible to transport beer over much greater distances and a number of huge brewing centres grew up. The biggest of them were London, Portsmouth and Burton-on-Trent. Gradually, most of the small town breweries shut down, as the brewery companies merged into large

Saracen's Head as it is today

Saracen's Head in the early 1920s

46

◁ Ye Old Farm House

Anglo-Bavarian Brewery, Shepton Mallet, circa 1900

combines, which produced their beer at just two or three places to supply the whole country.

Most pubs are now owned by breweries or brewing groups. The name of the company is usually on the sign outside, and if you ask the Reference Librarian at your Public Library he or she will be able to tell you where this particular company has its headquarters and where its breweries are. Then you can work out where the beer probably comes from. It would be interesting to try to discover exactly where the beer sold in a particular pub, like the Saracen's Head or Ye Old Farm House, came from at different times in the past, say, 1940, 1920, 1900 and 1880.

Pubs nowadays sell a lot of other things beside beer, of course. A good many tons of potato crisps, for instance, find their way to pubs each year, and pubs and the potato crisp industry have been very closely connected for more than sixty years.

Smiths Potato Crisps delivery vans, circa 1938

Index